Dance OF THE
Sandpipers

The
$\mathcal{D}ance$ OF THE
Sandpipers

Lessons from the Sea About Hope and Healing

To Laurie,
My dear friend.
Thank you for
your support!
Nancy Vason

Nancy Vason

MOUNTAIN ARBOR
PRESS

Mountain Arbor
Press
Alpharetta, GA

The author has tried to recreate events, locations, and conversations from her memories of them. The author has made every effort to give credit to the source of any images, quotes, or other material contained within and obtain permissions when feasible.

ISBN: 978-1-63183-189-8

Library of Congress Control Number: 2017958358

10 9 8 7 6 5 4 3 2   1 1 0 7 1 7

Printed in the United States of America

⊗This paper meets the requirements of ANSI/NISO Z39.48-1992 (Permanence of Paper)

For Hamp, Betsie, and Carlisle with love

Contents

Preface

I have always wanted to write a book. But until now, I never had a story that I felt inspired to share. This book was writing itself almost from the moment I learned that I had breast cancer. When I finally sat down to put my thoughts on paper, the first few chapters jumped onto the page. That encouraged me to continue. But then life got busier, and the rest of the chapters unfolded in fits and starts over the next ten months.

This is a very personal story. While it's easy to discuss life experiences with family and close friends, it takes more courage to share a personal story with people you don't know. I struggled to determine how broadly I wanted my story disseminated. I knew I wanted to express gratitude to all the people who had touched my heart during my illness, but was I willing to broaden my readership base in hopes that my words might help others?

After I gave the initial draft to my family for Christmas, our daughter, Betsie, returned her copy with some very helpful edits. She thought the book would resonate with cancer patients and encouraged me to reach out to them directly in my writing. She said, "Don't you want people who are going through cancer to read what you've written?"

I realized she was right. If you are a cancer patient or the friend or family member of a cancer patient, this book is for you. My story may be different from your own version of giant waves, high winds, or riptides, but I hope the lessons I have learned will have meaning and significance for you. I inserted notes at the end of each chapter to talk more directly with you about how you might apply these ideas.

I selected the sea as the thematic backdrop for my story because that is my place of rest, reflection, and healing. The beach also reminds me of the majesty of creation and the character of our loving Creator. A friend said she felt a gentle sea breeze as she read these pages, and I hope that you will too.

I am thankful for all the people who made my journey easier, which is many more than those mentioned in these pages. I am especially grateful to my family. They were my champions, providing love and support every day. I am also indebted to Laura Dabundo, my kind and patient editor, to Lucy Iloenyosi, who designed my book cover, and to the people of Mountain Arbor Press, who helped me publish my manuscript. In my view, they are all part of God's work in my life.

God's faithfulness is what inspired me to write this book. I hope as you read it, you will reflect on God's presence in your own life. I challenge you to trust Him with whatever difficulties you are facing, including your health. Then share this book with anyone you know who might find it helpful.

The Giant Wave

*It is the Lord who goes before you. He will be
with you; he will not fail you or forsake you.
Do not fear or be dismayed.*

—Deuteronomy 31:8

It was a peaceful, sunny day on St. Simons, a barrier island on the Georgia coast. The tide was still out, the temperature was perfect, and it felt great to be alive. My husband, Hamp, and I were out on the beach, lounging in our beach chairs and drinking wine. Sitting beside us were our friends, Marcia and John. The four of us were talking about life and kids. We have lived twenty minutes from each other in Atlanta for nearly thirty years and have shared many celebrations—from the births of our children to their college graduations, career choices, and wedding engagements.

One of us noticed a large cargo ship out at sea. These vessels carry cars and other imports from all over the world to Georgia. The water is quite deep just a few hundred yards out, so the ships can cruise along close to shore. They travel the same route at about the same time every day. We gave this ship a cursory glance, then continued our conversation.

All of a sudden, seemingly out of nowhere, a giant wave hit the shore, invading our sandy space. In one quick motion we grabbed up whatever our hands could hold and watched as everything else—beach bags, towels, shoes, and a portable cooler—were swept up by the wave and carried about twelve feet back toward the dunes. Wow! What a jolt! In an instant, the sand had shifted under our feet. As we were drying out my cell phone and trying to make sense of it all, the tide resumed its normal rhythm. What happened? And why didn't we see it coming? The culprit creating the giant wave must have been that ship, silently slipping past us. For the four of us, the afternoon was different after that. We pushed our chairs farther back from the water. We were more cautious now, more vigilant.

When breast cancer slipped silently into my life, it created a giant wave that jolted me to the core. I didn't see it coming. I was fifty-nine and healthy. I took no prescription medications. I'd been hospitalized only three times: once for a tonsillectomy and twice for the births of our two children, Betsie and Carlisle. I walked briskly along the three-mile path around our neighborhood park several times a week and avoided fried foods like the plague. The only villain in my family medical history was skin cancer—so I dreaded dermatologic checkups far more than mammograms.

I had been faithful about scheduling normal screening mammograms every year. Occasionally, I had been asked to return for a diagnostic mammogram and an ultrasound to investigate suspicious tissue. But the conclusion had always been the same: no problems. Thus, in late October 2014, when my gynecologist told me in my yearly checkup that she felt a lump, I was shocked.

What did this mean? My gynecologist tried to allay my concerns. "It may be nothing to worry about. Just schedule a diagnostic, and we'll see what's going on." I hoped she was right. After all, my mom had had benign lumps removed from her breast when she was in her fifties. She was now ninety-one and going strong. I kept my fears locked up in a little corner of my brain.

A week later, at the breast center, I had completed the diagnostic mammogram and sat waiting for my name to be called for an ultrasound. I noticed a flyer in the waiting room warning that one in seven women get breast cancer. Was I that one? "Lord," I prayed, "please, not me!"

After the ultrasound, a physician walked into the room where I sat to review the results. The look on her face and the tone of her voice told me all I needed to know: a giant wave was crashing into my life. She told me to schedule a biopsy immediately because she was concerned about both breasts. She warned me that I would be poked a lot. I left the breast center with a heavy heart.

As soon as Hamp came home from work, we talked about my fears. Hamp is the love of my life, a strong man and a very devoted husband. But he is clinical and matter of fact when dealing with health issues—not surprising for a dentist. He urged me to stay calm until we had the facts, but I could see both tenderness and worry in his eyes.

That night my mind swirled in a million directions. If I did have cancer, how serious was it? And what would happen to the life that I loved? I was happy in my marriage and excited to have both of our adult children back in Atlanta. Also, my work was rewarding. After years in corporate America, I had spent the last decade working as a coach at a communication-skills company called Speechworks. In addition to leading client workshops, I was teaching MBA students at Georgia Tech. I was also doing administrative work for Hamp's dental practice. And every month, I drove down to Cordele, the small South Georgia town where I grew up, to visit my mom. Mama was still adjusting to Daddy's death the previous year, and my sister, brother, and I were all trying to help. My life was full and I enjoyed it that way. There was no room for cancer on my calendar.

The next morning, my son, Carlisle, drove me to the biopsy procedure site on his way to class. He was living at home while applying to dental school, taking science classes, and working several part-time jobs. We didn't talk about what was ahead of me. But just before he dropped me off, he said he'd like to pray for me. His beautiful prayer was comforting. I can't remember all the words, but here's what I heard: "Lord, you are sovereign. You already know what's going on here. We look to you for strength, courage, and peace. We pray for positive news, but we know you go before us to prepare the way and will be with us, no matter what." How true! In good times and bad, I had always felt God's presence with me. But I had never been threatened by an adversary as vicious as cancer. Now more than ever, I needed God's strong hand holding mine.

As the procedure for the biopsy began, I kept silently praying the same words over and over: "Lord, help me deal with this. If I do have cancer, I pray that it has not spread." Meanwhile, I heard the radiologist's emphatic declaration: there had been a dramatic change in my breasts compared to the results shown on previous mammograms on file.

When the procedure was over, the radiologist said he found nothing of concern with my right breast. However, he reported two masses in my left breast.

"Do you think they are malignant?" I asked.

He wasn't about to say. But he told me if I were his wife, he'd want them removed either way.

I was shaky as I left the biopsy. Two days later, my suspicions were confirmed—the two tumors were malignant. I shared the news with Hamp and immediately called the office of a highly regarded breast surgeon. If I needed surgery, I wanted to get on with it. That weekend, while I was in Virginia to attend a wedding, the breast surgeon's nurse called with additional details.

"Your breast cancer is stage 2A," she said.

I asked her to translate.

She explained that one of the tumors was larger than two centimeters, but cancer had not spread to the ancillary lymph nodes. This last part was magnificent news, and I felt great relief and gratitude to God.

Thus began my journey, a journey of learning what it means to trust God with my health and to depend on Him for life itself. Little did I know then that the sea would be the setting for many of the lessons ahead. It all started with that giant wave.

If you have cancer, you probably didn't see it coming, either. Adversity is part of life, but that doesn't mean it's easy to accept. You may feel angry, depressed, fearful, or overwhelmed. Those are all normal reactions. But ultimately, you need to decide how you're going to adjust and move forward. I encourage you to ask God for His help.

2

A Great Egret in the Marsh

*Therefore encourage one another and build
up each other, as indeed you are doing.*

—1 Thessalonians 5:11

Golden Isles is the name given to the stretch of Georgia coastline that includes St. Simons and three other barrier islands, plus the port city of Brunswick. The grasses of the marsh are golden in color, and a wide variety of birds live in the marshlands.

My favorite marshland bird is the great egret, an elegant white bird that stands about three feet tall with a long, pointed, yellow bill; a long, thin neck; and lovely plumes. I typically notice egrets when I'm alone, riding my bike around St. Simons. When I spot them, I stop to watch and admire them standing tall in the marsh. They seem to thrive in this dynamic ecosystem of ever-shifting tides.

What do great egrets have to do with my breast-cancer journey? Well, a special person came into my life a week after my cancer diagnosis. In some ways, she reminded me of one of those great egrets. Here's how the events unfolded:

It was late afternoon, and I was on the interstate, driving south from our home in Atlanta to Cordele. I had a single purpose: to tell my mother that I had breast cancer. I was ten miles from Cordele when my breast surgeon's nurse called. I immediately exited the interstate and turned into a gas station to listen and take notes.

She said the rest of the pathology report was in, and there was a new finding. My breast cancer was aggressive, and I had something called HER2-positive. It sounded like a computer language to me, but it meant that my cancer required a new treatment plan. Instead of having breast surgery immediately, I would need to wait five to six months. During that time, I would have chemotherapy and receive a monoclonal antibody called Herceptin. Herceptin has been very effective in fighting HER2-positive breast cancer.

She asked, "Do you have an oncologist you'd like for us to call?"

The news hit me like a thunderbolt. I never dreamed I would need chemotherapy, and the thought of it terrified me. In my mind, chemotherapy was for really sick people. *I must be really sick!* Plus, I was devastated that my road to recovery would be significantly prolonged. I remember saying, "No, I don't know an oncologist. I'm at your mercy. Whom do you suggest?"

Then I went into emotional damage control. I couldn't just walk in and tell my elderly mother about this. Bad news is always toxic in the evening, when worry hijacks sleep. My news would have to wait until morning. So I visited with my mom as if nothing were wrong. Then I went to my sister Stella's house to spend the night. She already knew that I had cancerous tumors, but I didn't mention this latest lab report to her or to my brother Charles, who also lives in Cordele. I even withheld this new information from Hamp when we talked that evening. I was an actress appearing to be composed, while on the inside I felt brittle.

God and I had a direct line that night. I shared my anxieties, my fears, and the dread I was feeling at my core. I prayed fervently, asking for His help and guidance to get through this difficult time. I asked Him to hold me close and give me a sense of peace. After pouring out my heart, I was finally able to fall asleep.

First thing the next morning, I learned that my new oncologist could see me that day. I briefed my sister, then hurried to my mom's house and gently broke the news to her. I called Hamp en route back to Atlanta, filled him in, and asked him to meet me at the oncologist's office. The whole morning felt surreal.

At the appointment that afternoon, the oncologist was patient and kind, educating us and answering our questions. She explained the type of chemotherapy I would need, and said I'd have six treatments, one every three weeks. However, the Herceptin treatments would continue for a full year. In addition, she recommended that I receive another monoclonal antibody, Perjeta, until my surgery. I listened attentively, but I was still dazed. I told her I could think of only one friend and one cousin who had ever been through chemotherapy. Did she know anyone who had been through it who could help me navigate the journey?

"Yes!" she said. She had someone in mind who might be just the right person. She offered to contact her.

That night, the phone rang, and a friendly voice introduced herself as Ann. She said that she had the same type of breast cancer that I had. When she described her treatment plan, I realized it was just like mine. She was three months ahead of me and was in the middle of the chemo process as she spoke. I was struck by her upbeat, confident manner. I immediately started peppering her with questions. How are you feeling? Have you had many side effects? How's your energy level? Did you lose your hair?

She laughed and said we should go to lunch because we had a lot to talk about! So Ann and I met for lunch the following week in a little French restaurant that was convenient for both of us. She was tall and attractive and wore a fashionably styled wig. She was battling a cold, but it didn't seem to affect her spirits. She was cheerful, witty, and candid.

Ann told me that she *did* lose most of her hair, and the wig felt weird at first, but now she liked it. She felt good most of the time but had caught several colds because her resistance was down. As for side effects, she said food didn't taste very good, and chemo made her gums sore. She gave me a very soft toothbrush to use.

In addition, Ann said her energy level varied, but she had maintained her schedule of charity work. She thought it helped to stay busy. She also told me not to read about cancer on the internet because those articles would scare me. Instead, she recommended that I read *Breast Cancer Treatment Handbook* by Judy C. Kneece, RN, OCN.[1] This book had been very helpful to her, and she had brought a copy along for me.

What a gift from God! Ann was clearly an answer to my prayer for help. She and I continued to meet for lunch at that same restaurant throughout the next year. She always encouraged me and gave me just what I needed for the next part of my journey. Like a great egret, Ann is impressive. When I met her, she was adapting to the effects of the chemotherapy, just as an egret adapts to the rise and fall of the tides. But Ann didn't let cancer steal her joy. Instead, she stood tall and found a way to thrive despite her challenges. I watched Ann deal with her illness and I learned from her. She has been a wonderful mentor and friend, and she inspires me to this day.

---

[1] Kneece, Judy C., Renee Cannon, and Debra Strange. Breast Cancer Treatment Handbook: Understanding the Disease, Treatments, Emotions and Recovery from Breast Cancer. North Charleston, SC: EduCareInc.com, 2012.

*Mentors are wonderful for career develop-
ment, parenting, and fighting cancer. If you
don't have a mentor, look for one. Ask for
recommendations from your health-care
professionals, friends at work, or people in
your church or congregation. Having a
cancer survivor walk along beside you can
make your journey much easier.*

3

Thanksgiving Sunset

It is good to give thanks to the Lord, to sing praises to your name, O Most High; to declare your steadfast love in the morning, and your faithfulness by night.

—Psalm 92:1–2

When cancer strikes, both the patient and the family of the patient feel the effects. I knew that my journey of cancer and treatment would be hard on all of us, but especially on Hamp. When we initially talked about my diagnosis, he told me how much he loved me and that he would do everything in his power to help me get through it. But he couldn't talk about it all the time. It scared him too much to think he might lose me.

As for our children, I dreaded telling them that I had cancer. Our daughter, Betsie, was twenty-seven; Carlisle was twenty-four, and I didn't know how they would react. I could remember the horror I felt when I learned in my twenties that a favorite uncle had melanoma. He fought a valiant fight for several years but didn't survive. Our whole family still misses him. Then there was the time a few years ago when I got a frantic phone call from Betsie. Hamp and I were hiking out west near Jackson Hole. "Mom!" she said. "I have cancer!" In the next sentence, I learned that she had a very small basal cell carcinoma on her arm. She had it treated promptly, and it caused no harm, but it had scared her. My breast cancer fit somewhere between these two extremes. I could assure our children that most women survive breast cancer, especially if caught early. But no young adult likes to hear that a parent has a serious illness. Whatever their reaction to my cancer might be, I knew we needed to have a conversation about it, and I wanted to be the one to tell them.

We scheduled dinner at our house for a Sunday evening. I don't remember what we served, but I bet it was pasta. Hamp and I had lived in Italy early in our marriage when he was in the US Navy, and there's nothing like a big plate of *paglia e fieno* when you need some comfort food. We ate in the dining room so we could have a fire in the fireplace there. I thought we needed the warmth for our discussion.

Since Carlisle had driven me to the breast center for the biopsy procedure, he was concerned and eager to hear the biopsy results, but Betsie knew nothing. I had shielded her from the news during her friend's wedding in Virginia, and she was busy with graduate school at Georgia Tech and her part-time job. I'm not sure what I said to break the news that I had cancer in my left breast and would need chemotherapy and a mastectomy, but I remember Betsie's response: "You can be brave like Angelina Jolie. When she tested positive for the breast-cancer gene, she took immediate action and got both her breasts taken off." Wow! That was very to the point, just like Betsie. Carlisle was quieter, more reflective. They both asked a lot of questions. How was I feeling? Was I scared? What could they do to help? Hamp mostly listened, but the whole family rallied around me to offer support and love.

Once the news was out, we tried not to dwell on my illness. I went ahead with the required prerequisites for treatment. The magnetic resonance imaging (MRI) experience was a bit unnerving, but I distracted myself by recalling the great hymns from my childhood and singing them silently to myself. What could be more comforting than the words of "Amazing Grace" or "How Great Thou Art"?

The placing of my infusion port was the next step. The port is a small disc implanted under the cancer patient's skin right below the collarbone, with a plastic tube connecting the port to a vein. Having a port makes it easier to administer the chemotherapy. Carlisle took me for the outpatient procedure, and his girlfriend, Kelsey, who was in nursing school, stayed with me at home that afternoon. We both laughed when she gave me a big hug at the end of the day, and we felt our bodies knocking against the port. Oops! I had to learn to live with this new device on my chest.

During this time, I didn't seek a second opinion about my diagnosis or treatment. Three reasons in particular were persuasive. When I inquired within my network of contacts about my oncology team and my surgical team, everyone was effusive in praise. My selected provider, Piedmont Cancer Institute in Atlanta, is a certified member of the reputable MD Anderson Cancer Network. Finally, I wanted to get on with the fight—the sooner, the better.

My medical team and I agreed to start my treatments the week after Thanksgiving. Because trying to celebrate Christmas while on chemo might be unpleasant, I wanted a peaceful and happy Thanksgiving with my family. We agreed to spend the holiday on St. Simons Island and to treat ourselves to a Thanksgiving feast at the dining room of the King and Prince Hotel.

Thanksgiving Day was perfect. The weather was cool, beautiful, and sunny. I felt carefree because for the first time in years, I had absolutely no Thanksgiving cooking responsibilities. Our meal was not until midafternoon, so everybody relaxed beforehand. Carlisle went for a run, Betsie read, and we all watched the Macy's Thanksgiving Day Parade and the National Dog Show on TV. We cheered when the bloodhound won. He was our favorite because Hamp had grown up with a beloved basset hound. It was a day of simple pleasures.

At the King and Prince, we overindulged in the delectable feast before us. In addition to traditional turkey, dressing, and all the trimmings, the chef offered wonderful delicacies from the sea: smoked salmon, tuna, shrimp, and crab cakes. For dessert, we could have pecan pie, chocolate mousse, and macarons, Betsie's favorite. She ate at least a dozen of them.

After the meal, Carlisle suggested we talk about the things for which we were thankful. What followed was one of the sweetest hours of my life. Each of us spoke from the heart. Hamp and the children voiced their fears about my illness, their respect and admiration for me, and their determination that we'd all get through this together. I told them how much I felt God's presence in my life and how much I loved them. I had always played the role of mom, the nurturer, but now they were mothering me. I had never felt closer to my family.

Then we walked outside to take in the beauty of God's ocean and the miracle of a late-afternoon sunset. We took pictures and used one of them that year in our Christmas card. Life was sweet that day, and I felt God smiling down on us.

Sometimes it's hard to talk about our illness with the people we love the most. But when we are sick, they suffer too. They may even be at a loss about how to help. If you have cancer, I encourage you to engage in an honest discussion with your loved ones.

4

As the Waters Cover the Sea

But the earth will be filled with the knowledge of the glory of the Lord, as the waters cover the sea.

—Habakkuk 2:14

When word that I had breast cancer spread to friends from our church, they immediately reached out to me. Hamp and I have been members of Peachtree Presbyterian since we were newlyweds. This large church community in the city of Atlanta has sustained all our family, but especially our children. From the days when they ran the halls as preschoolers to their fun-filled, spiritually impactful summers at Camp Rutledge as teenagers, our children have always felt love and support at Peachtree. So have we.

First, I talked with a longtime church friend who is a cancer survivor. I remembered how brave she had been when she'd had a mastectomy several years earlier. She told me that breast cancer had been a blessing in her life. Really? I wasn't sure how that could be true, but she spoke of her closeness to God and her dependence on Him through the whole experience. She suggested that I have a healing-prayer service at our church before my surgery. She had done that, and said it was life changing.

Next, a member of the prayer ministry team called and came by for a visit. She brought me a prayer blanket. Members of the prayer ministry team take blankets to people in need, whether they are members of our church or not. My prayer blanket is bright pink and reminded me of the pink ribbon that is used to wrap gifts for newborn baby girls. I admit that I've never worn a lot of pink. It's not my favorite color. But pink is the color of the breast-cancer logo, so it seemed quite fitting, and I was glad to have it. In fact, during those weeks of chemotherapy when I was often cold, that soft, cuddly blanket was a godsend.

A patch sewn into the blanket contained this message: "To A Beloved Child of God. May you find the love of the Father and the peace, presence, and comfort of Jesus as you wrap yourself in this blanket. You are covered with our prayers and secure in His grace. 'I will never leave you nor forsake you.' Hebrews 13:5."

My visitor who brought the blanket also encouraged me to have a healing-prayer service. I promised to think about it, but I was hesitant. It wasn't that I didn't believe in the power of prayer. I absolutely did and had always felt uplifted when I had attended these services for others. But this was different. I didn't want a lot of attention focused on me. I was personally praying for God's healing, but I also wondered if a few friends might be leery of a service that had the word "healing" in it.

One of our ministers called. She also urged me to have a healing-prayer service. I've always been told that if you hear the same thing three times from three different people, you should pay attention. I told her I was considering it and explained my reservations. "Might someone unfamiliar with this service think it was weird?" I asked.

She laughed and told me it was anything but weird. In her experience, the service always brought healing of some kind, although not always physical healing.

After we hung up, I pondered this and then called her back. "Yes," I said. "I'd like to participate in a healing-prayer service, but I want to keep the service small and intimate."

About two dozen of us gathered at our church the day after I started chemotherapy treatment. Why that day? It was chosen because it worked for my family, but I believe it was divine timing. The previous day of treatment had made me acutely aware of the seriousness of my illness. After having lab work done and meeting with my oncologist, I had proceeded to the cancer infusion center, taken a seat in a big leather recliner, and watched the nurses administer one drug after another through the port in my chest. Between drugs, they had waited to make sure I wouldn't have an adverse reaction. The laborious process had reminded me of my fervent need for prayer.

Now, as I looked around at the people who had assembled for my prayer service, I felt comforted. My immediate family and my sister were there. Dear friends were there, as were several ministers and elders (governing members) from our church. After a few introductory remarks, the presiding minister read a Bible passage from the fifth chapter of James, said a prayer, and anointed my head with oil. Then the group drew closer, put their hands on my shoulders, and offered up individual prayers on my behalf. The prayers of my family were eloquent. They openly expressed their love for me and their confidence in God's providential care. Others asked God to strengthen me and give me courage. Some prayed for my physicians and surgeons, and many asked God to restore my body to good health.

I was not prepared for the deep impact this service had on me. It was holy. It was powerful. It was humbling. And yes, it was life changing. I felt a lightness in my step. I knew my family and I were not in this battle alone. Many people were praying for my healing and would continue to pray for me throughout my journey. The service filled my heart with hope and gave me deep assurance of God's love. You can hear my sense of awe in this excerpt from my prayer journal:

> *Dear Heavenly Father, how blessed I am. Help me always remember the love I felt surrounding me today. Help me always remember the dear and tender words spoken to you on my behalf. Help me treasure the promises repeated that you love me. I am yours. You are my rock, my anchor, my*

strength. You are the great Healer, the one who is stronger than cancer, and in your power can rid me of it . . . Lord use this sickness to change me into someone more caring, more loving.

I had a glimpse of the glory of the Lord that day.

Whether you are a praying person or not, I bet you know people in your circle of friends and acquaintances who are. It takes courage to ask someone to pray for you, but this one action can be life changing. God calls us to pray for one another, and having others pray on your behalf may lift your spirits and give you a sense of hope.

5

Three Wise Women

*She opens her mouth with wisdom, and the
teaching of kindness is on her tongue.*

—Proverbs 31:26

For me, the hardest part of going through chemotherapy
was losing my hair. It wasn't that I had a thick mop of hair
like Farrah Fawcett or beautiful Goldilocks curls. My hair
was short and straight, fine not coarse, and lay flat on top.
But it was my hair, and I was used to it. Losing my hair was
a tangible sign that I was sick, and I knew I wouldn't feel
whole again until it grew back. I read all about when I would
lose my hair and how to keep it for as long as possible. I
learned about a complex and expensive procedure that can
keep you from losing your hair during chemotherapy. In the
end, that process sounded like way too much trouble.

I finally decided I would have to purchase a wig, but what
kind? A human-hair wig costs significantly more than a synthetic wig. And while a human-hair wig looks very real, it
requires care just like your own hair—you wash it, blow it
dry, and style it. When it's humid outside, you might still

have a bad hair day. In contrast, a synthetic wig is more flexible. You wash it in the sink like a pair of hose. Then you shake it out, let it dry overnight, and presto! It retains its shape and looks as good as new. One small caveat: You shouldn't cook while wearing your synthetic wig unless you know that it is heat resistant. Otherwise, you may open the hot oven and singe your wig. Everyone suggested I get my wig promptly, since I was expected to lose most of my hair before the second treatment. Just what I wanted for Christmas, a fake head of hair.

I set out with Betsie to find a wig. The experience did not go well. Betsie tried to lighten my spirits by having me try on all sorts of wigs, including a mop of straight dark hair that came way below my shoulders. I looked in the mirror and to my horror, I saw a haggard witch without her pointy hat. Betsie took a picture of me and sent it to Hamp, who told Betsie to destroy it as quickly as possible. No one wanted that picture to turn up on Facebook. I realized why I couldn't find a wig that day. I was still in denial that I was really going to lose my hair.

I shared my frustration with my friend Mary, a cancer survivor who had lost her hair while undergoing chemotherapy ten years earlier. She offered to go with me to look for a wig. A few days later, we entered the wig shop together. The first wig I tried on was a blonde synthetic wig. It matched my color well, and it fit the shape of my face. That's when Mary gave me some wise advice. "Nancy, it looks great, and I think you should buy it. You don't need to go through any more stress over this. You can always get another wig later, but this one is a keeper." With her vote of confidence, I bought the wig. But when I placed it on its plastic stand in our bedroom, I stared at it like an unwanted stepsister. Was I really going to have to wear that silly thing?

The hairdresser in the wig shop had told me to come back before my next chemo session so she could shave my head and place the wig on top of my head. The day of the appointed head shaving was still two weeks before Christmas. My hair was thinning, but most of it was still there. I decided I just couldn't do it. I wasn't ready to look like a tennis ball that had lost all its fuzz.

I called my hair stylist, Jennifer, who also gave me wise advice. "What you need," she said, "is a very short and sassy haircut. When your hair comes back in after chemo is over, you'll need to get used to wearing it very short. This will be the perfect time to try it out." With that, she snipped and clipped and left me looking quite chic. In fact, when I showed off my new hairdo to my family, Carlisle's girlfriend said I looked "edgy." Now that's a high compliment.

Thanks to that timely cut, I made it through Christmas Day with my own hair. What a relief!

The day after Christmas, we headed down to St. Simons. By that morning, I knew my hair had to go, but I didn't know a hairdresser on the island. I thought about walking into the barbershop. Surely, someone there could deliver a buzz cut with style! Instead, I called a friend who knew the perfect person for the job. I walked into the Serendipity Spa-Lon and asked Amanda if she would buzz cut my hair. Amanda gave me some wise advice. She told me to come back at the end of the work day, when all the other customers had left. "That way," she said, "I can take all the time I need to do a great job, and you will have complete privacy." How lovely she was to think of my dignity!

I returned later that day, as directed, and put my fate in the hands of this petite blonde stylist. She asked me if I wanted to buzz the sides and keep the top a little funky. "No," I said. "I love your passion for fashion, but just buzz it the same length all over. After today, I'll be wearing my wig."

She worked slowly and carefully so I wouldn't get a single nick. She asked me about my family and treated me like a friend instead of a stranger whose entire head of hair was drifting onto the floor. By the end, I didn't feel like a bald tennis ball; I felt like a normal person who happened to be wearing a buzz cut.

Three wise men are featured in Matthew's Christmas story. They come to see the Christ child and bring him gifts. But in my life, three wise women appeared at Christmastime. Each gave me wise counsel. My friend Mary gave me the gift of her presence. Because she had been through chemotherapy, it was comforting to have her with me. My hair stylist Jennifer gave me the gift of her talent, creating a short, sassy haircut that carried me through Christmas Day. My seaside stylist Amanda gave me the gift of kindness, not only taking great care with my buzz cut, but also showing that she cared about my feelings and my pride.

I believe all three wise women were gifts from a loving God.

If your treatment includes chemotherapy, you may or may not lose your hair. Ask your oncologist what to expect. If you do lose your hair, don't lose heart! You have lots of options—wigs, hats, scarves, ball caps, or no head attire at all. Whatever you decide, remember that people can still find the real you inside.

6

High Tide, Glad Tidings, and Riptides

Therefore be imitators of God, as beloved children, and live in love, as Christ loved us and gave himself up for us, a fragrant offering and sacrifice to God.

—Ephesians 5:1–2

One Monday night a few weeks before Christmas, Hamp came home with news. "Michael (Betsie's boyfriend) called me today at work," he said, "and wanted to stop by tonight."

"Hamp," I replied with a smile, "you know what that's about. Michael wants your blessing before he proposes to Betsie!" Mothers know these things.

Sure enough, that night our future son-in-law appeared in the kitchen, excited and eager, clearly on a mission. Within five minutes, he had declared his deep love for our daughter and his desire to share his life with her. After receiving the nod of approval from his future father-in-law, Michael smiled and relaxed, and the three of us had a heartwarming discussion about marriage, faith, hopes, and dreams. I felt thrilled to be a part of that conversation and admired the way Michael handled himself. It's still a sweet memory for me.

Michael was planning to propose around New Year's Eve. For almost a month, we were conspirators keeping the big secret. Finally, on December 30, Michael arranged a romantic dinner on Sea Island near St. Simons and asked Betsie to be his wife. She was delighted. She called us the next morning brimming with excitement.

For Betsie and Michael, their engagement was a high-tide event. It signified a positive change in both of their lives, complete with all the optimism that comes with the promise of building a loving future together.

For me, the engagement represented glad tidings. Betsie and Michael are a great team, and their personalities complement each other. I was thrilled that they had made a commitment to marriage. I was excited that they planned to reside in Atlanta, and their engagement reminded me that joy often comes in the midst of difficulty.

A few days later, Betsie and I had our first conversation about the wedding. That's when I felt the strong riptides threatening family peace and good will. The undercurrents were pulling us in different directions. The first point of contention was the date. Betsie and Michael wanted to get married sooner rather than later, and I wanted them to wait until autumn to give me time to heal and grow my hair back. (Yes, this was all about me!) Then there were concerns about how big the wedding should be. They preferred a small wedding, but Hamp and I both had big families and many longtime friends. Last, there was the difficulty of finding a suitable reception site. Again, we had different visions. Was there anything on which we could agree?

Betsie and I have always been close, but all this wedding talk strained our relationship. She was very busy with grad school and her job and wasn't interested in wedding details. She also didn't want me losing sleep over the wedding (which I was doing the first few weeks). Her solution was to let the wedding planner handle everything. Of course, I wouldn't hear of that. I thought the mother of the bride (known around wedding circles as the MOB) was supposed to be involved in the details. Plus, planning the wedding was a great distraction. It kept me from thinking about those cancer cells inside of me. It offered other benefits as well:

❖ It kept me busy and provided a creative outlet during the months of chemotherapy when I didn't have enough energy to teach daylong classes at Speechworks.

❖ It facilitated enjoyable lunches with seasoned MOBs who offered lots of wisdom and free advice!

❖ It helped me reconnect with family members as I searched for addresses and called them to share the plans.

Betsie and I survived the riptides by focusing on how much we loved each other. Some days were tense, but others were full of joy, like the day Betsie found her wedding dress.

When I was a young bride, I had missed the pleasures of shopping for the dress. Instead, I chose to wear my sister Stella's dress and veil. Her lifelong friend, Anne, had helped Stella select the veil from Priscilla's of Boston, where Anne worked at the time. Since then, Anne has become an accomplished and well-known wedding-gown designer. So, on a cold February day, Anne graciously met Betsie, Stella, and me at the Atlanta shop that sells her Anne Barge wedding gowns. Together, we watched Betsie try on one beautiful dress after another, until she found the *Downton Abbey*–style gown that was perfect for her. Then, at Betsie's request, we pulled out the heirloom wedding veil. As Betsie tried it on with the dress, her face lit up and she said, "I love it!" Stella and I were thrilled, knowing that the same veil that had graced our weddings would be going down the aisle with Betsie as well.

High-tide moments, glad tidings, and riptides are all part of life. So is love—the love of two sweethearts, the love of a mother and daughter, and the love of two sisters. God understands all of this. He is right there in the middle of our joys and our challenges, loving us and teaching us how to live in love.

Just because you have cancer doesn't mean the world stops around you. You may have happy events or difficult challenges in your life—and likely, both—while you battle your illness. Try to keep things in perspective and remember that life is not just about you. If you can keep love at the center of your relationships, that will help immensely.

7

A Seagull Standing on One Leg

For you have been my help, and in the shadow of your wings I sing for joy.

—Psalm 63:7

My husband has always been a beach guy. When we were younger, and someone asked him where he'd like to live after retirement, he never hesitated. "I've got to be near the beach," he'd always say.

The older I get, the more I agree with my beach guy. One of the things I like most about the beach is sitting in my beach chair, watching the pelicans and the gulls. The pelicans are quite impressive as they crash vertically into the ocean with the intensity of fighter pilots, seizing their prey and racing back into the sky. Gulls are less dramatic. They take flight when they see fit, and they soar with a dignity and effortlessness that amazes me. But they also stand still on the beach for long periods of time with their faces turned toward the wind, seemingly contemplating life.

I, too, contemplate life when I'm on the beach. Sometimes I even contemplate the life of gulls. Their patterns are beguiling. Usually, they stand on the beach on both legs. But sometimes, like pelicans, they stand on one leg. Who knows why? If you research this question on the internet, bird experts will explain that gulls, like many other birds, stand on one leg to rest the other leg and also to stay warm. By tucking one leg under their feathers, they significantly reduce the amount of heat lost through their unfeathered limbs.

When we were at the beach in January, I watched a gull stand on one leg for so long that I thought he must have only one leg. He seemed to be normal otherwise—no other signs of illness or injury that I could see. I found myself wondering, *What happened to him? Is he handicapped by having just one leg? How long has he been like that? Will this condition shorten his life? Is he still able to fly?*

Then I realized the source of my interest. I had one normal breast and one that was diseased. I felt a little like a gull with one leg. I had been undergoing chemo, and I was feeling the effects. I had lost most of my hair, and I was wearing a cap to keep from losing body heat. My nose was running constantly because I had lost my nose hairs (an unpleasant byproduct of chemo). I had lost weight. Consequently, I wondered what my life would be like after chemo and surgery. Would I be less attractive? Worse still, would cancer shorten my life? Would I always feel threatened that it might come back? I had been full of energy and vigor before this experience. When this was all over, would I be forever cautious, afraid to live life fully—afraid to fly?

In the midst of my thoughts, I recalled a Bible scripture about birds. The passage is Matthew 6:25–26: *Therefore I tell you, do not worry about your life, what you will eat or what you will drink, or about your body, what you will wear. Is not life more than food, and the body more than clothing? Look at the birds of the air; they neither sow nor reap nor gather into barns, and yet your heavenly Father feeds them. Are you not of more value than they?* I wasn't worried about food or clothing, but I was concerned about the future. I knew God was looking after me. I wanted to believe that I still had many happy days of good health ahead of me in this life. But the truth is, that's not for us to know. What I do know as a Christian is that God is faithful and promises to be with us, no matter what. He gives us strength, even when we are weak. And I know that my life here on earth is not the end of the story.

Suddenly, the one-legged gull took flight. He soared with other birds, and I couldn't tell if he had a genuine handicap or if he'd been pulling my leg. It didn't matter. I had my answer. God didn't want me to lose heart. He wanted me to trust in Him and face the future with hope. He wanted me to believe that I could still fly!

Many of us sometimes worry about the future. If you are battling cancer, you may feel especially anxious or depressed. If that's your situation, I encourage you to reach out. Share your feelings with a health-care professional or seek counseling. Try journaling. Finally, read Bible verses and be reminded of God's providential care for you.

8

My Flock of Pink Flamingos

*As God's chosen ones, holy and beloved,
clothe yourselves with compassion, kindness,
humility, meekness, and patience . . . Above
all, clothe yourselves with love, which binds
everything together in perfect harmony.*

—Colossians 3:12, 14

Shortly after I found out I had cancer, a friend told me about Pink. This support group for women with breast cancer is part of the Thomas F. Chapman Family Cancer Wellness program at Piedmont Healthcare, Atlanta. It includes exercise classes three times a week. The Pink program had helped my friend, so I thought, *Why not?* It was free and would give me a chance to work on my abs.

In February, I joined the thirty-first Pink class at the Piedmont Atlanta Fitness Center. I admit, it sounded as if I had joined a military squad. We women in Pink 31 came from different backgrounds. We had different life stories and circumstances, but a common goal. We were all fighting a fierce and crafty enemy: cancer.

I'll never forget the first day that our group of ten women met together. Ann, my mentor, was there, but all the others were strangers to me. We were asked to introduce ourselves and tell a little bit about our personal journeys. Instead of the normal, polite niceties you might expect, the testimonials these women shared were candid. Some were a bit startling—about surgeries gone awry, cancer that came back, needy and nonsupportive families, depression, isolation, helplessness, and fear. But the women also shared stories of resilience. They spoke of strengths they didn't know they had. They described setbacks and recurrences and how they had pushed to find the right physicians and get the treatment they needed. These women were brave and they were tough.

As I listened to the cancer survivors, who, like me, were still in the heat of battle, I was deeply affected. First of all, I felt a bit guilty, because my journey seemed easier compared to some of theirs. I had my attack plan to battle cancer, and, so far, it was working. I had my faith, which was helping me stay positive and peaceful. I also had the double blessing of a wonderful family and a large network of supportive friends. But I also felt a deep kinship with these women. They were living through difficult times in their lives, and each one was finding a way to cope and heal. I was doing the same thing. We understood one another, we respected one another, and we admired one another. Most of all, we needed one another. That's a solid basis for friendship.

During the next three months, while I was going through chemotherapy then preparing for breast surgery, I met several times a week with these women to exercise and talk. Over time, my military squad took on a very different character. We were less like a group of soldiers and more like a flock of pink flamingos!

Flamingos are water birds found in southern Florida and along the Gulf Coast but also in the Caribbean, the Yucatan, South America, and on islands like the Galapagos. They are social and gregarious and clearly enjoy one another's company. They trust the other birds in their flock. They are good at reading cues, and they learn to move in sync.

That's the way we were. We greeted each other with smiles and offered lots of helpful hugs. We laughed together and joked about our Pink T-shirts and fashion wigs and efforts to keep our hair. We complained about the rigors of the exercise and complimented one another's efforts to make our bodies strong. We talked about diet and power foods and about letting go of caregiving duties so we could take better care of ourselves. We commiserated about the fact that once you've had cancer, you're forever on guard and nostalgic for the life you used to have. But we also celebrated one another's positive steps toward wellness—whether it was completing the last session of chemotherapy, improving a person's diet, or adopting healthy behavior. Mostly we cheered one another on.

Shortly before my breast-cancer surgery, I found a big surprise waiting for me when I arrived at Pink. One of the sweetest women in our class had, with her daughter, created a portable, stand-up bulletin board for me. In pink chalk, she had written the number of days until my surgery, with an eraser to change the countdown number every day. She had attached visual images and words of encouragement to the board, including a big, bright sun and the words "Laugh" and "You are awesome!" I loved it. It was one of the purest acts of kindness I have ever received.

Another remarkable event happened just before my surgery. One of the women in the Pink group came up to me privately at the end of class and said, "I know from our discussions that you are a person of faith. I am, as well. One of your surgeons was also my surgeon. I wanted you to know that he prayed with me before my surgery, and it gave me a great sense of peace." Yes, Pink is one of the great blessings of my breast-cancer journey.

What did I take away from this experience? It affirmed for me what research already says is true: People are social animals, and we need other people—to listen, to encourage, to support, and just to walk along beside us. Particularly in times of challenging health, social connections and friendships make a significant difference in the body's ability to heal and move forward. I think God is very much at work in these relationships, placing people in our path to minister to us and to give us the privilege of ministering to them. He can use our experiences to accomplish His greater purposes when we allow people into our struggles.

My flock of pink flamingos has scattered, but the bond we shared lingers. I offer my heartfelt thanks to the courageous ladies in Pink 31.

Support groups come in many forms. I encourage you to find a group that works for you. It takes courage to open up about your feelings. My experience shows that it's healthy to do so.

9

Sunshine Glistening on the Water

You are the light of the world . . . Let your light shine before others, so that they may see your good works and give glory to your Father in heaven.

—Matthew 5:14, 16

One of the gifts from the beach that I enjoy the most comes on clear, sunny days, when I look at the ocean and see the sunshine glistening on the water. What a beautiful sight it is—so glorious it makes me feel that God himself is laughing down from heaven, and Louis Armstrong is singing "What a Wonderful World."

When I was going through chemotherapy, Hamp and I went to St. Simons often on weekends. We agreed that the sea was therapeutic for me. Each time, I would take my chair out on what we named "Nancy's Beach" and look west toward the late-afternoon sun and the Jekyll Island bridge. On special days, the sunshine would begin its dance of glee, glistening like sparkling diamonds on the water. As I watched, I could feel my spirits lift.

Back at home, the love and warmth I received from my friends and extended family gave me that same euphoric feeling. I have always protected my privacy, but I told people about my cancer because I knew I needed support and prayer. I was amazed that so many people took the time to reach out in very tangible and helpful ways.

One clear example of glistening sunshine came from the Sole Sisters. The Sole Sisters are ten of my dearest friends. We met over thirty years ago when we and our spouses joined the Couples in Christ Sunday school class at church. Our affection for one another grew as each of us became mothers. Social get-togethers evolved from wine-and-cheese parties to Memorial Day family retreats and annual Easter egg hunts. We shared spiritual fellowship and parenting advice and brought gifts and food whenever a new child was born. We even discussed tips for how to conceive a boy versus a girl.

As our children grew, our friendships deepened. Over time, some of the Couples in Christ members migrated to other churches closer to their neighborhoods, and our Sunday school class merged with another class. But we women stayed close. As our children became teenagers, the Sole Sisters were born. The idea of wearing fashionable shoes inspired the name, but soul sisterhood bound us together. The Sole Sisters were among the first friends that I told about my breast cancer. That's not surprising, since the Sole Sisters stand by one another through both the joys and challenges of life.

When I shared my news, the Sole Sisters cried a few tears, gave me long, reassuring hugs, and then sprang into action. I was touched when one of them appeared at my door in January with a delicious, home-cooked meal. The next week, another Sole Sister knocked on my door with flowers and a care package. The next week, still a third Sole Sister arrived, bringing food, good books, and music to lift my spirits. By the fourth week, I knew who was at the door. A few weeks later, I heard the official name of their very well-organized and intentional caregiving: Operation Sunshine.

For ten weeks during my chemotherapy, Operation Sunshine brought joy into my life. Often, when the Sole Sister of the week would deliver gifts, she would stay and chat; I loved our visits. The Sole Sister might inquire about my health but never treated me as if I were sick. She would share news about her kids or share pictures and stories about her grandchildren. She would listen to the details and drama of the Vason wedding plans and offer sound advice or tell me to lighten up.

In addition to the Sole Sisters, I experienced glistening sunshine from breast-cancer survivors. This group is like a great big sorority, but the members welcome you into their bond without credentials or a secret handshake. Their specialty is empathy, and their support is unwavering. Before my cancer diagnosis, I never realized how many friends and acquaintances had experienced breast cancer. Every one of them reached out to me by phone or email to be of help. Some had had mastectomies, and a few had been through chemotherapy. They were all great sources of advice and inspiration.

Many other people outside my immediate family brought sunshine to me. The list goes on and on, but here are a few examples:

- ❖ Friends took me to chemo sessions. Sometimes they chatted quietly, and sometimes they entertained me with stories. Each friend gave up a whole day to keep me company.

- ❖ Two first cousins arrived at my house for a "Sunshine Weekend," bringing homemade soups, fresh vegetables, cheese wafers, and boiled custard—all my favorite things.

- ❖ My friends at Speechworks sent flowers for my surgeries and included me in all social events even during the chemotherapy months when I cut back on work. My fellow coaches sent cards and gifts and took walks with me.

- ❖ Friends from my church and other churches prayed regularly for me, day after day. They wrote out scripture verses, brought meals and flowers, called to check on me, and sent cheery emails and encouraging cards. Some days I had so much mail I felt like Santa Claus.

Because of all this love, I felt that sunshine was glistening all around me. That sunshine came from the heart of God. He was watching over me, and His love was made evident through the many people who cared for me. Just as I was the recipient of sunshine during my cancer journey, I now want to be on the giving end of Operation Sunshine. There are a lot of people in this world who need light and warmth and hope—and not just cancer patients. My prayer is that God will show me how to glisten in the light of His love and share that love through tangible acts of kindness.

While battling cancer, you may not have the large network of support that I had, but I bet you have people in your life who love you dearly. I hope you will tell them about your cancer and let them give you support. I am very glad that I let people in. Sometimes we all need to lean on others. Then, when we are stronger, we can let others lean on us.

10

The Battered Conch Shell

But those who wait for the Lord shall renew their strength, they shall mount up with wings like eagles, they shall run and not be weary, they shall walk and not faint.

—Isaiah 40:31

I am a collector of seashells. I always have been, and likely I always will be. For years on our family beach vacations, I'd take long walks with Betsie, and together, we'd search for shell treasures. We'd wash them, admire them, and choose the most stunning to bring home. Betsie has always favored tiny shells, beautiful but delicate, while my favorite has always been the conch shell. Maybe that's because, when I was a little girl, my great aunts told me that if you put the conch shell up to your ear, you could hear the sea. And I could! What magic for a child who loved the beach.

I always talked of making a seashell lamp with our collection, but instead I have vases, baskets, and candleholders filled with sea shells. They are lovely to me, each one different in color, shape, size, and texture. I still look for conch shells on the beach at St. Simons, but conch shells are rare there, perhaps because of the way the sea curves around this barrier island.

One day in March, Hamp and I were walking toward the end of East Beach, where the water from the ocean meets the river and the marsh, with Sea Island just to the north. A conch shell caught my eye from a distance, and, with great excitement, I rushed over to pick it up. I was immediately disappointed. It was not the treasure I had imagined. Instead, it was battered and broken, well worn by the ravages of the sea. I started to let it go, then changed my mind. I took it back to where we were staying, washed it off, and kept it. It might not be as beautiful as the other conch shells in my collection, but the shell had made it to shore. Based on its appearance, that was no small feat. If it could speak, I'm sure its story would be well worth the hearing. In those days, I felt a little like that conch shell. Not very attractive. Not very robust. A bit battered in spirit.

My treatments were not painful, but they wore me down, a little more each month. My body suffered. Food tasted like metal, and I paid a price for whatever I ate. I didn't have much appetite. For people who know me, that's hard to imagine. By spring, I had lost fourteen pounds. Also, my skin was so dry I felt like a prune. I drank more water each day than I had ever consumed in my life, but all that moisture seemed to evaporate from me. People gave me wonderful gifts of body lotions, creams, and natural soaps, but my body still seemed parched.

My physical appearance suffered as well. In addition to losing the hair on my head, my face was missing eyebrows and lashes. Before chemo, my eyebrows had been coarse, wiry, and unruly, like a blonde/gray version of Groucho Marx brows. Good riddance to those. But my lashes had been long, and with the right mascara, they had accentuated my eyes. Now they were gone. Then there were my nails. Brittle always, they didn't respond well to chemotherapy. In spite of soaking my fingernails and toenails in ice during treatments, I ended up losing the nails on both of my big toes. No sandals or open-toed shoes for me.

To make matters worse, my body was unpredictable. The steroids before, during, and after chemotherapy made me hyper and full of energy. After my first chemotherapy session, I hurried home and decorated our Christmas tree. But on other days, I'd spend two hours running errands and come home utterly exhausted. One day, I was in a boutique retail store looking for earrings when I suddenly grew so faint I dropped down to the floor to keep from passing out. Another time, while enjoying a holiday lunch with work associates, I got so cold I had to take the throw blanket I had opened as a gift and wear it over my shoulders.

My last chemo treatment was the week after my sixtieth birthday. By then, the cumulative effect of these drugs was apparent. When I look at pictures of my birthday celebration, I feel sad to see how pale and unhealthy I looked.

But like the conch shell, I made it to shore. I didn't enjoy the chemo, but I got through it. Once the treatments were over, my appetite returned. And in late spring, because I was still skinnier than normal, I bought my first bikini in years. Okay, maybe it wasn't a bikini by today's standards, but it was a skimpy two-piece—and I actually wore it on the beach. Who needs long eyelashes in a bikini?

The point is this: most of us are jostled around and worn down by life from time to time. The difficulties take their toll on us, physically and emotionally. But if we are fortunate and land safely on shore, we have a story to tell. Our story helps others get through tough times. And as good health returns, we are more thankful, appreciative, and joyful than before.

I continue to pick up shells whenever I am at the beach. My collection now includes more broken shells, fragments, and shells with imperfections. I'm a lot like those shells now, and so are my friends. It's impossible to get through the high winds and crashing waves of life unscathed. But we all have rich stories to share.

Chemotherapy affects people differently, so don't let my experience scare you. If you go through it, you'll learn how your body reacts and adjust accordingly. Be sure to follow doctor's orders regarding water intake, protein consumption, and all the rest. And remember, this strong medicine should help you regain your good health.

11

In Search of Calm Waters

Come to me, all you that are weary and are carrying heavy burdens, and I will give you rest.

—Matthew 11:28

By April, the tumors had shrunk, but they were still there. I was still recovering from chemotherapy, but it was time to think about surgery. I needed to build up my strength. I talked to a nutritionist about eating the right foods. I walked diligently around my neighborhood and attended Pink exercise classes. I also wanted to prepare my mind and heart for what lay ahead. I needed time to read, rest, and pray.

My husband, Hamp, was depleted as well. He seemed extra tired from the demands of his dental practice and in sore need of a vacation. He had been wonderful to me throughout those months—considerate, patient, and supportive. He had helped around the house and kept a positive attitude toward me and everyone else. But watching me battle cancer had taken a toll on him. Like many men, Hamp doesn't like to discuss his concerns, but I could see that he was burdened by my cancer. His fears for my long-term health stayed just below the surface. He felt powerless to fix the problem, so he prayed and put his trust in God. Nevertheless, he needed to get away and have some fun.

In Atlanta, beach lovers are either Atlantic or Gulf people. The Atlantic has bigger waves, hard-packed sand, and enchanting marshlands. The Gulf has softer, white sand, translucent, blue water, and a calmer surf. Hamp and I have always preferred the Atlantic. So why did we choose to go to the Gulf? We were searching for calm waters.

Yet when we arrived, Clearwater, Florida, was teeming with people. Every square inch of beach seemed to be occupied with a tent, an umbrella, a beach chair, or a blanket. We scouted out a space just big enough for our two chairs and umbrella. To our right were teenagers and young adults with tattoos, bikinis, beer, and music. To our left was a Hispanic family crammed inside a giant tent. It had at least twenty people from four generations under it, looking as if it might burst at the seams from all the activity. The family was having a wonderful time. Our favorite in their group was an adorable toddler squealing with delight from the "Johnnie Jump Up" toy that was suspending him in space. It was fun to be in the middle of American culture—a reminder that people of every age and gender and ethnic background enjoy the beach. But as Easter Sunday approached, I wondered if we'd find a church amidst these sunglasses, towels, and sandals.

The Chapel-By-The-Sea did not disappoint us. When we walked into this lovely church on Easter morning, we were greeted by sunshine beaming through the windows and beautiful white lilies spread all over the sanctuary. Then the choir entered with voices that sounded like angels from heaven. The music soared up to the rafters and reverberated through the pews, ringing out in celebration of the resurrection of our Lord. I felt content and thankful that Christ made this day possible. Because He sacrificed His life for our sins and conquered death, I, as a believer, could approach God not only as Father but also as Lord, Savior, and Friend. I wasn't thinking about dying or even about eternal life. I was inspired to be a better person in this life in response to His boundless love.

Although our time in Clearwater was energizing, we were spinning a bit from the whirlpool of spring breakers, Easter vacationers, and snowbirds all around us. We still needed peace and quiet, and we found it in the deserted beaches further south. We stopped briefly at Holmes Beach, where we enjoyed a leisurely sailboat ride with my cousin and his wife. Then we unpacked our bags at Casey Key, where my good friend Debbie had invited us to spend several days. Her sister owns a beautiful property there and was gracious to share it. The house where we stayed looked out on a lovely lagoon. The ocean was just across the street. What a great place to slow down. We slept late, lounged in the pool, and read our books. We took long walks on the beach, and I hunted for shells. We enjoyed grilled fish and fine wine every night. With all that good seafood, my appetite made a remarkable comeback.

By the time we returned home, Hamp and I felt new vitality and optimism. We were well rested and relaxed. We had talked about our fears and our hopes for the future. We were more committed than ever to each other and to the road ahead—from surgery to full recovery.

The beach and waters of the Gulf, the Chapel-By-The-Sea, and the hospitality of friends and family calmed our spirits and soothed our souls. I thank God for His part in all of that.

Cancer is tough on the whole family. Spouses need relief from stress just as the cancer patient does. Getting away for a few days can help. If you can, discuss each person's needs ahead of time. You may want to spend your vacation together, as we did, or you may decide that a break from each other is just the right medicine.

12

Venturing out to Sea

And when he got into the boat, his disciples followed him. A windstorm arose on the sea, so great that the boat was being swamped by the waves; but he was asleep. And they went and woke him up, saying, "Lord, save us! We are perishing!" And he said to them, "Why are you afraid, you of little faith?" Then he got up and rebuked the winds and the sea; and there was a dead calm. They were amazed, saying, "What sort of man is this, that even the winds and the sea obey him?"

—Matthew 8:23–27

Fishermen seldom venture out to sea when storms are brewing. Swimmers are warned not to venture out to sea at night—it's far too risky. But sometimes in life, we all must venture out to sea. I've always been risk averse. I don't dream of jumping out of airplanes or hang gliding. Once, in my twenties, I refused to go parasailing, even though it looked like great fun. The riskiest thing I've ever done was to float above the ground in a hot-air balloon!

But when the time came to make decisions about my breast surgery, I felt risk. I knew that I would have a mastectomy of the left breast. My surgeon had advised me that the tumor locations required this approach. But should I have surgery only of the diseased breast, or of both? This was uncharted territory for me. I didn't want to venture out to sea without a compass, so I consulted other people. I talked with my medical team, with other women who had experienced breast cancer, and of course with Hamp, because this decision would affect both of us.

Clearly, there were potential high winds with either choice. The bilateral (double) mastectomy would be tougher and require a longer recovery, but it wouldn't be twice as hard. The long-term effect on my body would be more dramatic—I'd be losing a perfectly healthy breast. As for reconstruction, any risk associated with implants would be twice as great since I'd have two of them. However, with reconstruction on both, I would have greater symmetry and the chance to look like Dolly Parton. (Wow!)

But what if I left the healthy breast alone, and then cancer was found to be growing there later? That seemed like a bigger risk. My oncologist told me the chance of having this specific type of breast cancer show up in my other breast was very slim. I was more likely to have bone cancer or a tumor in my brain (discouraging news, to say the least).

I talked with a friend who had had both a bilateral mastectomy and hysterectomy preventively once she learned she had the breast-cancer gene. A counselor said she knew more women who regretted *not* doing the bilateral mastectomy than those who were sorry they did. Other women are very comfortable with the decision to leave their healthy breast intact. In the end, I realized there was no right or wrong way to go. I had to make the decision that seemed best for me.

I prayed earnestly about this and decided to have the bilateral mastectomy. I wanted to minimize the chance, however small, of another breast-cancer episode. I didn't want to live in fear of future mammograms. Maybe because of the trauma of going through chemotherapy, I wanted to be proactive. I felt at peace with my choice, and so did Hamp.

Once I had charted my course, two steps remained: getting through surgery and healing from it.

During the days leading up to surgery, I stayed busy with wedding plans, bill paying, and physician appointments. Although I had completed chemotherapy, I was still on two drugs, Herceptin and Perjeta. They were injected through my port every three weeks. I didn't miss a treatment.

I also tried to spend time with God every day. I read Bible passages that would nourish me during the week of surgery. I asked the Lord to keep infection away and to help me trust in a positive outcome, instead of focusing on the what ifs. My biggest fear was that my surgeon would find cancer in my lymph nodes. Part of the surgical procedure is to check the sentinel nodes. If those are clear, that is great news. If they are not, additional samples must be taken to determine if the cancer has spread.

My family and friends, together with my great surgical team, created a safe harbor of support. The night before surgery, my breast surgeon called and said not to worry—he would take good care of me. Early the next morning, my plastic surgeon prayed with me before the presurgical procedures began. In those moments, I felt an amazing peace and, surprisingly, no fear. During the surgery, Stella and Carlisle were in the waiting room praying for me. Other family members and friends were praying as well.

The surgery went beautifully. One tumor had not responded to the chemo as well as the other tumor had, which was troubling. But my skilled surgeon removed all the cancerous tissue. Best of all, the sentinel nodes were clear! How thankful I was to hear that news.

In a few days, I was back home, healing. The surgical site looked better than I had expected. I had drainage tubes to manage, but I was prepared for this; my breast-cancer friends had offered supplies and suggestions to help. I was not in excruciating pain. I was just weak, uncomfortable, and sore.

I didn't slow down for long. By Saturday, I concealed my drainage tubes and strolled down to a neighbor's house to watch the Kentucky Derby. I stayed just long enough to hear "My Old Kentucky Home" and see the race. Then I headed home, exhausted.

On Tuesday of the following week, my plastic surgeon removed several of the drains. I was thrilled with my progress and felt blessed beyond measure.

For three weeks after my surgery, I didn't cook a single meal. The food train that had been organized by friends worked seamlessly—so well, in fact, that Hamp was hurrying home from work to see what the food angels had brought that day.

My venture out to sea turned out to be less treacherous than I had feared. But even if the winds had been higher or the waves more menacing, even if I had had unforeseen complications, I still would have trusted God to see me through. Why wouldn't I? After all, He is the Captain who can master the rough seas. He is our source of strength and hope.

If you need surgery for breast cancer, your medical team will make recommendations and offer options. I recommend you take time to weigh the options, pray about them, then move forward with confidence.

13

Ponte Vedra

Praise the Lord! Praise the Lord, O my
soul! I will praise the Lord as long as I live;
I will sing praises to my God all my life
long.

—Psalm 146:1–2

Ponte Vedra Beach, Florida, a seaside community just south of Jacksonville, is named for a Spanish port city of similar latitude, Pontevedra. The word Pontevedra means "old bridge." Our family vacationed at Ponte Vedra Beach, Florida, for more than fifteen years with our good friends Martha and Craig and their daughter, Casey, and son, Scott. After my surgery, when we all returned to Ponte Vedra Beach, I felt as if I crossed the bridge from breast cancer toward full recovery.

The Ponte Vedra tradition began in 1988 when our little girls were toddlers. Our sons forged an enduring bond with the salt air, the deep beaches, and the roaring waves of Ponte Vedra in the summer of 1990 when they were still babies in our wombs. I was six months pregnant and looked like a beached whale. Martha was four and a half months pregnant and looked like a model who barely needed a maternity bathing suit. We were both grumpy because we couldn't drink margaritas, but our boys didn't notice. They were inside of us, kicking for joy just to be at the beach.

Ever since, Ponte Vedra had been our happy place where we left our cares behind. I remember lazy days and fun-filled nights. For the kids, there were shark-tooth hunts, boogey-board adventures, pet-crab races, frisbee throws, kite flying, and cartwheel tumbles on the beach. For the adults, there were golf outings, tennis lessons, best-selling novels to read, and long walks and talks on the beach.

Years later, after our sons had graduated from college, they instigated the reunion trip. They were relentless in their campaign to get our families back to Ponte Vedra again. We marked our calendars a year in advance and started making plans. We didn't know that breast cancer might spoil the fun. My surgery occurred less than four weeks before our trip. I was nervous that I might not be healthy enough to go. As it turned out, it was perfect timing. I knew it as soon as we unloaded our luggage and walked out on the deck. The view of the ocean was stunning, and the sound of the breakers was cathartic. I could feel peace and contentment washing over my soul.

All eight of us were thrilled to be back. Our kids had grown up, inch by inch, on these shores. Now they were young adults with promising careers and engaging personalities. Meanwhile, we parents were older and wiser. This reunion week was a chance for us to relax, rejuvenate, and celebrate the significance of this beach for all of our lives.

Having eight adults share one beach house is challenging, but everybody respected one another's need for space. Fortunately, this house offered places to socialize and quiet spaces for solitude. We could lounge on the beach or on the deck or walk down to the nearby pool or gym. Sometimes I retreated to our bedroom to rest.

For me, Ponte Vedra provided healing. I walked the beach every day. As the week progressed, my walks got longer and my pace grew quicker. We women took several mother-daughter beach bike rides, and I found my stamina better than expected.

I also cherished the one-on-one time with our kids. Betsie and I talked about her future with Michael and her career. Spending time with her was a gift because we both sensed that our relationship would change once she married in September. Carlisle, meanwhile, was almost at the end of his gap year between college and dental school. He would be leaving home soon, and I was going to miss him. This week allowed me the opportunity to tell him what he had meant to me during my illness.

Each of us carved out time to be alone, but when we did get together, we had a great time. At night, beach music wafted from the portable speakers on the deck, and sometimes we danced. This tradition began when the kids were little, and Martha and I would hold our sons in our arms and shag to all our favorite beach tunes.

One night, Scott showed us his smartphone app that identified the stars. We had a glorious view of the night sky from our deck, so we started gathering to stargaze and talk. We reveled in the quiet beauty of the heavens and the powerful roar of the ocean.

On the last night of the trip, we renewed the one tradition that we never seemed to outgrow. We gathered up the tools of the trade—flashlights and big buckets—and headed out to the beach in search of crabs. It was a group effort, for sure. We had runners, spotters, crab chasers, and bucket holders. But the star of the show, as always, was Casey. As a former high school soccer star, she was the quickest, the most agile, and the most daring. Crabs never had a chance against her deft use of Solo cups to scoop them up.

At the end of the hunt, we eased the crabs back into the water, then retired to the house to relive the thrill of the chase. We reminisced about all the years of screaming, "There's one—go get it!" and the annual capture of Big Bertha, the biggest crab of them all.

When I think back on this reunion trip, I am in awe of how special it was. Why is that, I wonder? Certainly, the setting was inspirational: the ocean, the shoreline, the gulls and pelicans, the occasional dolphin jumping through the water, the beaming sun, the cloudless sky, the magnificent stars, and the gentle ocean breezes. But ultimately, the week reflected the sweetness of life itself. It brought back memories of the excitement we felt as new parents and the wonder of watching our children grow. It reminded us that we had raised good kids who were now confident, caring adults with hopes and dreams of their own. In an instant, one generation of young adults had given way to the next, and we had seen it happen before our eyes.

We all have Ponte Vedra moments in our lives—exceptionally happy times that are so dear to us that we keep the memories forever in our hearts. Those moments are the reason we work so hard to stay healthy and fight so hard to restore our health when illness strikes. We yearn to keep living because life, at its best, is wonderful. We strive to live honorable lives because we have been blessed.

God understands all of this. He is the Creator and Sustainer of life. To God be the glory for all of life's precious moments and for life itself.

Recalling positive experiences and savoring the sweet memories of life can be therapeutic when you are experiencing illness. Naming all the things for which you are thankful is helpful, as well. Try it, and remember that God is the source of our blessings.

Driftwood

*Thus says the Lord, who makes a way in the
sea, a path in the mighty waters . . . Do not
remember the former things or consider the
things of old. I am about to do a new thing:
now it springs forth, do you not perceive it?
I will make a way in the wilderness and
rivers in the desert.*

—Isaiah 43:16, 18–19

After the trip to Ponte Vedra, I felt invigorated and
stepped up my activities. I started taking on more work. I
went to Savannah twice for June weddings. I continued our
own wedding preparations. But during those months, strange
things were happening to my body. I progressed from having
flat breasts that hardly warranted a letter in the alphabet
(barely size A) to trying to figure out just how many letters I
wanted in my future (C cup or double D).

All of this change is labeled reconstruction, and the for-
eign objects making all this possible are called expanders. A
tissue expander is like a temporary implant placed between a

woman's skin and her chest muscle. It stretches the skin so the body can later accommodate a permanent implant. Using a port, the plastic surgeon adds a saline solution to the expanders periodically over several months, until the expanders reach a size that is close to the final implant size. Then the expander is surgically removed, and the implant is inserted in its place.

The expanders are slightly uncomfortable. At first, I felt as if balloons were being pumped up inside of me, and I hoped they wouldn't pop. Of course, the process is scientific and safe. The changes happen very gradually, and after a while, I hardly noticed the expanders. But at some point, I had to decide where to draw the finish line.

I have never envied women who were exceptionally well endowed. Big breasts might turn some heads, but at my age, I wasn't expecting many craned necks. Plus, who wants to carry all that extra weight around? I just wanted to be me again, and I wanted my old clothes to fit. So that's the goal we set for reconstruction.

The bigger issue was how I would fit implant surgery into my life. The earliest that surgery could be scheduled was late July to give the expanders time to do their job. The latest possible date was mid-August, so I could heal in time for Betsie's wedding. Between those two dates, we had scheduled a business trip to Oregon for a dental association meeting. When my surgeon heard about the Oregon trip, he ruled out late July. He said it would be unsafe to maneuver luggage so soon after surgery. So the date we picked was August 17, a week after we would return from Oregon and less than four weeks before the wedding.

That's when the texts and phone calls began. My caring family thought I was making a mistake. My mom voiced her concerns to my sister, who felt the same concerns and relayed those to me. My sister-in-law texted me that she, too, was worried. They all said it was too close to the wedding. What if something went wrong? Would I ever forgive myself if I wasn't healed enough to enjoy the wedding, or, worse yet, if I were unable to attend? It was a risk, but it's what I wanted to do. I was on a mission to get back to normal, and implant surgery was the next step. Why delay another two months? But in case I was being unwise, I called my surgeon for a consultation. He reminded me that this surgery was minor compared to my April surgery. He felt confident I'd be able to dance at the wedding. That's all the reassurance I needed.

We flew to Oregon in early August. Before we met up with the other dentists, we spent a couple days driving along the rugged Oregon coast. We drove right into the heart of Oregon's beautiful and very dense forests filled with Douglas firs, massive redwoods, cedars, and spruce. Close by the national forests are small, sandy beaches studded with rocky headlands and crashing waves.

One of the beaches that caught my eye was Driftwood Beach. When we found it, the beach was deserted and quite beautiful. The driftwood deposited there varied in size, shape, and texture from small, one-foot pieces to massive logs. I was struck by the idea that the grand trees of the forest, which seem strong and permanent, could be damaged enough by storms (and loggers) to be uprooted and washed down rivers and streams, then swept into the ocean and, ultimately, onto Oregon's beaches. Once removed from the forest, the wood is no longer in its original form, but it is still useful. It protects the beaches from erosion, provides shelter for birds, and inspires collectors who fashion pieces of art from the debris.

Here, among these powerful forces of nature, I saw parallels with my own situation. I was trying to recover from my own personal storm, finish reconstruction, and get back to normal. It suddenly hit me that the idea of normal is an illusion. Life is about change and adapting to new circumstances and new realities. I would never have my natural breasts again. As much as I wanted my implants to make me feel like myself again, the surgery scars would always be there. My life was permanently altered, and I had to adjust to a new normal. This transition and full acceptance of the new normal would take time. But I knew that once I recovered from implant surgery, I'd still be able to lead a useful, purposeful life—just as those trees still have function and purpose after their shape and form have changed.

I returned from the August trip with a new perspective on change. A week later, when I woke up from surgery, I welcomed my new body parts and gave thanks for skilled surgeons. A few weeks later, I danced with joy at Betsie and Michael's wedding.

Adapting to change is hard. Naturally, we feel sad about the losses that come with cancer. It's not healthy to get stuck looking back. Instead, be resilient. Decide that change offers new possibilities and embrace the new you.

15

The Lord Bless You
and Keep You

The Lord bless you and keep you; the Lord make his face to shine upon you, and be gracious to You; the Lord lift up his countenance upon you, and give you peace.

—Numbers 6:24–26

Surely there is no more exciting event in the life of a family than a wedding. For the mother of the bride, the challenge is to make sure the stress of the wedding production doesn't steal happiness from the couple's big day. Every mom I know dreams that her child's wedding day will be filled with joy. September 12 was such a day for us. As my sister-in-law wisely told me, "By the time the wedding arrives, you've done all the preparations you can. It's time to relax and enjoy it."

As the day dawned, the first good omen was the weather. After raining most of the week, the clouds vanished. The air was crisp with the first hint of fall, and I took a vigorous walk before noon. That walk was golden—a time to relax and reflect on the significance of what was about to happen in the life of our daughter.

Betsie designated our house to be wedding central for makeup and hair preparation, so by noon we were quite busy. Michael had encouraged all the bridesmaids to keep Betsie on schedule so she would not be late to their wedding. My own preparations were amazingly easy because I didn't have to worry about my hair. My brand-new wig was sitting on its wig stand, and all I had to do was put it on my head and let the hairdresser fluff it a bit and spray. For months, I had dreaded not having my own hair for the wedding, but now I realized that donning a wig for the wedding day was a great timesaver and stress reliever.

Meanwhile, at a local hotel in Midtown Atlanta, a small drama was unfolding with my now ninety-two-year-old mother, the grandmother of the bride. For months, Betsie and I had waged an intense campaign to get Grandma to attend the wedding. She had not been to Atlanta in ten years, and after much pleading, she had agreed to come. But that morning, she was battling a stomachache. Lying on the bed with a hair bonnet on her head, she was wringing her hands and saying, "Well, I declare. I will just have to miss the wedding." Her absence would have been a major disappointment to Betsie and all of us. Thankfully, between 10 a.m. and 4 p.m., with the help of her caregiver and my cousin, she made a miraculous recovery. She maneuvered her walker into the chapel lobby just as I was emerging from the bridal suite. We guided her inside to see Betsie decked out in her wedding dress and looking beautiful. The photographer was summoned and Mama stood to her full height and smiled for the camera. There we were, three generations of strong women, sharing a precious moment for the ages. What a blessing.

The wedding itself was sacred and special. As I looked around, it struck me that the witnesses gathered in that chapel were the most important people in Betsie and Michael's lives. So it was fitting that the crowd clapped in approval as the newlyweds recessed down the aisle.

What happened next touched my heart. When Carlisle returned to the front of the chapel and began escorting me out, the crowd started applauding again. I was stunned. They were celebrating my return to health and expressing their joy in sharing this happy moment with me.

At the reception, the celebration continued. We had good food and wine, a wonderful band, and a rousing rendition of "The Good Old Song" by the bridal couple and other University of Virginia alumni.

Two events stand out. The first was Hamp's ad-lib toast to the absent bride and groom. After all Michael's efforts to keep Betsie on time, she was late to her own wedding feast. The wedding planner told Hamp they were on their way, so he took the microphone, quieted the crowd, and prepared to announce the entry of Mr. and Mrs. Michael Hollister. But the bridal couple didn't come and didn't come. So Hamp began his toast, thinking they would appear any second. Since the delay continued, the toast went on much longer than planned. Meanwhile, Betsie was backstage, brushing her teeth—a fitting excuse for the daughter of a dentist.

The second event was very special to me. After the bridal couple danced, Betsie danced with her dad, and Michael danced with his mom, Carlisle offered a blessing for the food. Then he turned to me and said, "Mom, wanna dance?" Of course I did! Carlisle is an impressive dancer, and like most mothers, I was thrilled to dance with my son, even if it was not his wedding day. There we were, with the stage all to ourselves and everyone looking on, while he led me through some twists and spins. All of a sudden, right at the end of the song, he did a signature Carlisle move and dipped me! Sounds like fun, right? But there was just one problem— I had on my wig! As he lifted me back upright, I grabbed my head to make sure the hair was still up there. Thank goodness, it was. Can you imagine my face if the wig had ended up on the dance floor?

Memories like these are priceless. But what I will remember most about the day was the pure exuberance on Betsie's face—her eyes glowing with a bright light and her smile radiating with excitement. She was absolutely beaming. My sister, who has directed hundreds of weddings, said Betsie was the happiest bride ever.

The wedding ceremony's final hymn sums up the sentiments of the day. Betsie had asked three of her bridesmaids to sing John Ritter's arrangement of "The Lord Bless You and Keep You" as a benediction. These bridesmaids had been in chorus together in high school, and the chorus always ended its performances with this hymn. But at the bachelorette party on St. Simons, they had pushed back, saying that their voices were not professional enough. Betsie insisted. She told them not to sing to all the wedding guests but simply to sing to her. So with the help of two young male musicians from our church, a tenor and a bass, the bridesmaids sang their hearts out. It was sweet, reverent, and powerful. It was also a perfect prayer for Betsie and Michael, asking God to bless their marriage.

As I listened, I had a thankful heart. God had indeed blessed my family and been gracious to all of us during my battle with cancer. On Betsie's wedding day, he had lifted up the light of His countenance and reflected that light on the face of my daughter. On what could have been a stress-filled day, He had filled me with a sense of peace.

A wedding is a day of celebration. For the bride and groom, it's also a day of commitment. In a leap of faith, they pledge themselves to each other as they go forward into an unknown future. When you are battling cancer, you don't know what the future holds either. But if you put your faith in God, He will bless you and give you peace.

16

Harvest Moon

*For everything there is a season, and a time
for every matter under heaven.*

—Ecclesiastes 3:1

Fall is when the University of Georgia plays the University of Florida in football. Attending the Georgia-Florida game is a seasonal ritual for Hamp and me. For decades, we have shared this tradition with our good friends, Ann and Mike. Our friendship began when we were all students together at the University of Georgia. And believe it or not, Ann and Mike have only missed a couple of Georgia-Florida games since college.

The game itself is always played on a Saturday in late October in Jacksonville, Florida—supposedly a neutral site. But the Georgia-Florida weekend is about much more than the football game. For Hamp and me, it's about driving down to the Georgia coast and reuniting with a number of our closest college friends who join us there. In the old days, we'd eat shrimp, drink beer, and play touch football on the beach (like the Kennedys). Now we eat fresh fish, drink wine as well as beer, and *sit* on the beach, swapping stories and laughs.

This particular October, the Georgia-Florida weekend took on new meaning for me. That's when I gathered up the courage to abandon my wigs. By this point, I owned three wigs: the original fashion wig, the dress-up wig I wore to Betsie's wedding, and my inexpensive, everyday wig. The wigs had been a royal pain at first, but they had added levity to my cancer journey. For example, there was the winter evening when, teaching business communications to MBA students, I was in the back of the classroom, video recording their presentations. Over several minutes, I realized my wig was slipping farther and farther back, leaving my nearly bald forehead exposed! I was mortified that my students might notice, so I declared an unscheduled break and bolted to the bathroom for an emergency wig adjustment.

At other times during chemotherapy, the absence of a wig had caused me trouble—like the day I was home paying bills and decided to make a quick trip to the bank. I jumped in the car, drove down our street, waved at two neighbors, and then realized they had just seen my bare head. Yikes! No wig! I turned the car around and retrieved my wig before venturing out again.

But the most embarrassing wigless moment happened one night early in my cancer treatment when I was dressing to go out for the evening. Realizing I needed a blouse from the laundry room downstairs, I bolted down the stairs, turned the corner, and nearly collided with Carlisle's girlfriend, Kelsey! Obviously, I didn't know Kelsey was visiting. She had never seen me wigless. I laughed and said, "Just passing through," and kept moving.

By the Georgia-Florida weekend, I had grown enough hair to kiss those wigs goodbye. Since I was among friends, I felt comfortable letting my hair down—even though my very short hair stood on top of my head looking like a curly crew cut. That weekend, I also had exciting news to share with these college friends. A month earlier, Carlisle had proposed to Kelsey. Some thought Betsie's wedding must have inspired Carlisle's decision, but Hamp and I knew better. Carlisle had realized some time back that Kelsey was his soul mate, and we had watched their relationship mature and deepen during the year that Carlisle lived with us at home.

In early August, he had asked me to help him shop for the perfect engagement ring. By the time he left for dental school, that ring was burning a hole in his pocket. As eager as he was, he had agreed to wait until after Betsie's wedding to propose. But he didn't wait long. Betsie and Mike were still on their honeymoon when he and Kelsey announced their engagement. That's a guy in love. I was looking forward to being the mother of the groom—a much easier role to play than MOB. Best of all, I would have a wonderful new daughter-in-law.

On the Thursday night before the Georgia-Florida game, I was quite content as Hamp and I joined our friends for an oyster roast. The setting was an outdoor pavilion and dock overlooking the marsh. This place is special any time of year, but the combination of good weather and an inviting fire pit made it the perfect site for an October get-together. Several of us walked out to the dock just as night fell. Suddenly, we nearly gasped as we noticed the immense orange ball dominating the night sky and illuminating the golden marsh. We agreed that it must be a harvest moon, although technically harvest moons appear in September or early October. All I know is that it was so grand and so beautiful that I will never forget the sight of it.

As I feasted on the beauty of this so-called harvest moon, I realized that my own life had entered a new moon phase, a season of harvest. The hard work of healing from cancer was yielding results. My hair had grown enough to stop having to cover it. My family was growing too, and we were about to welcome another new member into the fold. I had much for which to give thanks.

Yes, fall is the season for football. Every football season, Georgia plays Florida. The outcome determines whether our team is having a good football season or a disappointing one. But in life, we sometimes don't notice when one season is ending and another is beginning. In my case, a beautiful moon in the autumn sky reminded me that my season of breast cancer was nearing its end. Wellness and wholeness were on the horizon, and that was good news indeed.

As you go through your cancer journey, I hope you'll find lighter moments when you can laugh. I hope you will also experience seasons of improvement, or at least some hopeful signs. Celebrate those occasions with your friends and loved ones.

17

The Lighthouse

*Therefore, since we are surrounded by so
great a cloud of witnesses, let us also lay
aside every weight and the sin that clings so
closely, and let us run with perseverance the
race that is set before us, looking to Jesus,
the pioneer and perfecter of our faith.*

—Hebrews 12:1–2

I've always been attracted to lighthouses. There are many
historic lighthouses dotting the coastlines of both the Atlantic
and the Pacific. Whenever I see one that is open for tourists,
I like to ascend the steps to the top and look out at the vast
expanse of sea it services with its light. The structure of lighthouses and the technology they use for signaling have
changed in modern times. But lighthouses always have the
same mission. They use a very bright light, called a beacon,
to bring navigational aid to ships at sea and to protect them
from danger.

Of course, lighthouses are manmade, but I have always
felt that God serves as a lighthouse for those who believe in

Him and seek Him. When we sincerely look to Him for help and direction as we navigate our lives, He will be there for us, casting light on our path and providing a steady, constant source of strength on which we can count.

I was very aware that God's light had been guiding my life through my months of illness and recovery. I was a follower of Christ long before cancer struck me, but my health crisis led me into a deeper, more intimate relationship with the Lord. Why? Because I was totally incapable of fighting cancer on my own. I had to relinquish my sense of control (which is very hard for me) and depend completely on God. That meant praying daily, reading scriptures, and continually seeking the direction of the Holy Spirit. God answered, guiding me through every decision, bringing the right people into my life at just the right time, and gracing me with His presence so that I never felt alone.

As October turned into November, I started thinking more about the future. I prayed that God would protect me from further illness. I also wanted Him to illuminate my way forward. During this time, I still didn't know why cancer had presented itself in my life. I may never know. But I began to think that maybe the Lord had some work in mind for me—some way that I could serve Him through my experience. I wanted the fog to clear so I could see what God wanted me to do.

In early November, I heard Margaret Feinberg speak at our church. She is an excellent writer and inspirational public speaker who battled breast cancer for several years. In fact, I had heard her speak once before, when she wore a hat as a symbol of her experience with chemotherapy. After listening to her speak this time, I was struck by the way God was using her talents for His glory. It made me feel that I had not finished the work He had in mind for me.

The idea had popped into my head months earlier that perhaps I could write about my experiences. I even had several chapter titles in my mind. Now I found this thought creeping frequently into my prayer journal: "Lord, help me move forward to do the things you want me to do, whether it is writing a book or serving others more actively." "Lord, help me with my inertia and my lack of energy and motivation to begin writing."

Slowly, I started to tell people that I wanted to write. Hamp was supportive. So were my children. I shared the goal with a close friend and asked her to hold me accountable to make a start. There was a problem: I had never written a book. I was a journalism major in college and had written a few magazine articles over the years, but I was best known for writing an annual Christmas poem for friends and family. I wasn't sure I had the talent to write a book, nor was I sure anyone would read it.

Thus, I tabled the idea. But the desire to capture my story on paper didn't go away. Instead, I felt an increasing sense of urgency to record my experiences and emotions before time dimmed my memories. I knew my story would not be a page-turner like a suspense thriller. But it would be a chance to express my gratitude to God for His faithfulness during my time of need. I hoped that if I shared my story, others might be drawn to His light.

My book project would not begin for a couple more months. But on Thanksgiving weekend, I looked up at the stately white lighthouse on St. Simons Island. I asked God to inspire me and embolden me to tell my story. I asked Him to give me the courage to start and the perseverance to finish.

If you have battled cancer, think about all you've learned. Is there a way that your experiences might help others? If you're not sure, ask God for guidance. You may be surprised at the opportunities you suddenly see to use your talents for good.

18

Safely in the Harbor

Those who love me, I will deliver; I will protect those who know my name. When they call to me, I will answer them; I will be with them in trouble, I will rescue them and honor them. With long life, I will satisfy them and show them my salvation.

—Psalm 91:14–16

December arrived, marking the passage of a full year since my treatment for breast cancer had begun. As I looked back, I remembered the life-changing healing-prayer service that had inspired me to hold fast to my faith and take God's hand for my journey. I recalled the burst of energy I felt on the day of my first chemo treatment when I decorated our Christmas tree. But I also remembered disappointments, like missing a Christmas concert because I felt sick, and catching the flu because my immune system had been compromised.

Now I was approaching the holidays with a positive sense of well-being. I was busy finding the best family picture from the wedding to share in our annual Christmas card. I was touring possible rehearsal-dinner sites with Carlisle and Kelsey as they planned their wedding. I was chatting with Betsie about getting the extended Vason family together on Christmas Eve. In short, I was preparing for Christmas with the kind of energy and purpose that characterized my life before cancer. But I still had two important physician visits on the calendar: my last Herceptin treatment at the Piedmont Cancer Institute and a follow-up appointment with my breast surgeon. They were in mid-December, two days apart.

My appointment at Piedmont began uneventfully. A sample of my blood was taken, and I had a short visit with my oncologist. We talked about my progress and agreed that my curly hair was coming in nicely. She confirmed that, since my infusion treatments were ending, the port in my chest was no longer needed. As always, she was encouraging but reminded me to stay vigilant in monitoring my health. We agreed on quarterly visits going forward. I thanked her for the excellent care she had given me.

Then I went downstairs to the infusion center and settled into one of the leather recliners—familiar territory by now. Every three weeks for the past year, I had received cancer-fighting drugs in this room. As usual, I was greeted by the oncology nurses and assistants who always seemed to exude a quiet, caring professionalism as they carried out their duties. Their pleasant voices, ready smiles, and helping hands had worked like a salve to calm me in those anxious first days of chemotherapy. They were extra friendly and jovial today, knowing it was my last treatment. Since I was only receiving

Herceptin, the process took less than an hour, and before I knew it, they were disconnecting the tubes and smiling down at me. "You're all done." What magical words those were!

As I was thanking the last nurse for her help and gathering my things, she said, "Don't forget to ring the bell as you leave."

I looked at her quizzically. "What do you mean?"

"Oh," she replied, "it's a tradition here. Whenever patients complete their final treatment, they get to ring the big bell that's over there, right by the exit. You should do it!"

I made my way toward the exit, found the big bell on the wall, and after just a second's hesitation, I smiled and rang the bell—several times I think. As soon as the sound rang out, everyone in the infusion center stopped, clapped, and cheered for me.

At that moment, tears of joy started streaming down my cheeks. I had hardly cried in all the months of my illness. Now the tears appeared out of nowhere—a totally unexpected, spontaneous response to the great sense of relief and lightness of spirit I felt. I guess the significance of what had just happened sank in. My journey was over. I had navigated through the course that was laid out for me, and I had arrived safely in the harbor.

Two days later, my breast surgeon and his nurse, the same person who had first told me my tumors were cancerous, removed the infusion port from my chest and wished me a merry Christmas. I thanked them both for their skill and professionalism and, especially, for their caring spirits, which had made my journey much easier.

Throughout history, when ships arrived safely back from sea, the town bells rang out in jubilation. The people of the community gathered at the water's edge to celebrate and to give thanks. In the same way, my mighty band of medical professionals let me ring the bell, and my large support community of friends and family cheered and gave thanks to the Lord when my ship came in to shore. I cried tears of joy and gave thanks as well.

If you are currently fighting cancer or dealing with another health challenge, I hope with all my heart that you make it safely into the harbor after your illness. Remember that none of us navigate this journey alone. I encourage you to thank the kind people who help you along the way. I hope you'll also give thanks to Almighty God.

Epilogue

The Dance of the Sandpipers

May the God of hope fill you with all joy and peace as You trust in Him, so that you may overflow with hope by the power of the Holy Spirit.

—Romans 15:13 (NIV)

The winter-morning air was cool on our faces as Hamp and I walked vigorously along the shoreline of St. Simons beach. The tide was coming in, but the sand still extended way out from the land, forming a vast playground for all of nature to enjoy. It was early, and the beach was practically deserted. The only sounds we heard were the steady clap of waves reaching the shore, the whistle of the wind, and the occasional screech of gulls flying overhead. We were approaching the end of East Beach, where we typically pause to take in the view before turning around and walking back toward the village.

On the beach between us and the dunes, several hundred sandpipers—it seemed like a thousand—were all bunched up together as if they had gathered for a family reunion. They stood body to body, feather to feather, as still as statues, as if frozen in time.

All of a sudden, a frisky black Labrador retriever came running with reckless abandon right into their midst. In the blink of an eye, they abandoned their poses and took flight, rising up into the sky like a squadron of military jets. With amazing synchronization, they dipped their wings first to the left, then circled back to the right, forming an elegant figure eight. Because their back feathers are dark gray and their underbellies are white, their bodies kept changing color as they swirled and turned, catching the light of the sun and creating a kaleidoscope of colorful patterns. It was a dance of sheer beauty and grace, and I stopped walking, enchanted. I felt as if I could hear the choir singing "The Hallelujah Chorus" from Handel's *Messiah* in the background. What a masterful performance. It filled my heart with joy.

I believe God choreographed this grand spectacle. Was it for His glory or maybe just for His pleasure and for ours? Who knows? But in that moment, I felt a great connection with the Lord Almighty. I felt that He was sending me a message: "Life is very precious. My world is a place of beauty and splendor and hope. I am in charge, and I care deeply for all of my creation—the birds of the air, the fish of the sea, and, yes, I care deeply for you. I love you, and I want you to love others and be joyful!" And why not? Why should we live our lives laden with fear or worry about our health or anything else? Isn't it far better to acknowledge God as the source of our hope, take His hand, and let Him show us the joy and wonder that comes from walking with Him in faith?

I know this sounds simplistic. Perhaps it's easy for me to propose this idea because my own battle with cancer turned out well—at least so far. Other people I know and admire greatly have fought this enemy called cancer with courage and faith, and their stories have ended differently. But the truth is that none of us is going to live forever on this earth. We can try to exercise, eat right, and take care of ourselves, but we can't predict the length of our lives, how healthy we'll be, or how much we'll suffer before we die. What we can determine is our response to the circumstances that present themselves in our lives and whether we are going to fight our battles alone or put our trust in God. I believe our Heavenly Father wants us to know Him, love Him, and serve Him. He sent His Son, Jesus, into the world to offer His saving grace to all who believe in Him. If we accept this gift of grace, we can experience the joy and peace that comes from knowing Jesus as Lord, both in this life and for eternity.

I learned a great deal from my year of cancer, and, yes, the sea was the setting for many of those lessons. The one truth I treasure the most is the certainty that God will not let us down. Just as we can count on the tide to come in and go out every day, we can count on Him to be with us and guide us through the storms of life.

He is worthy of our adoration and trust. He is powerful enough to tame the seas and gentle enough to hold us close when we are scared. He lavishes us with blessings and delights in seeing us happy. He grieves when we are hurting. And, yes, He is the great Healer who cures our diseases but also purifies our hearts, so that we can lead joyful, meaningful lives and share His love with others.

To God be the Glory!

About the Author

Nancy Vason has enjoyed writing since her college days at the University of Georgia, where she graduated magna cum laude from the Henry W. Grady College of Journalism. A lifelong learner, she has two master of science degrees, one in business administration from Boston University and one in education from Georgia State University. She has spent much of her career helping corporate leaders become more effective communicators. She is an executive coach at Speechworks in Atlanta and is on the faculty at the Scheller College of Business at Georgia Tech.

Nancy's greatest joy comes from the relationships in her life as a wife, mother, daughter, sister, and friend. She and her husband live in Atlanta. They enjoy traveling together and spending relaxing weekends on St. Simons Island.